DEATH BY CHOCOLATE

ALAN NOLAN

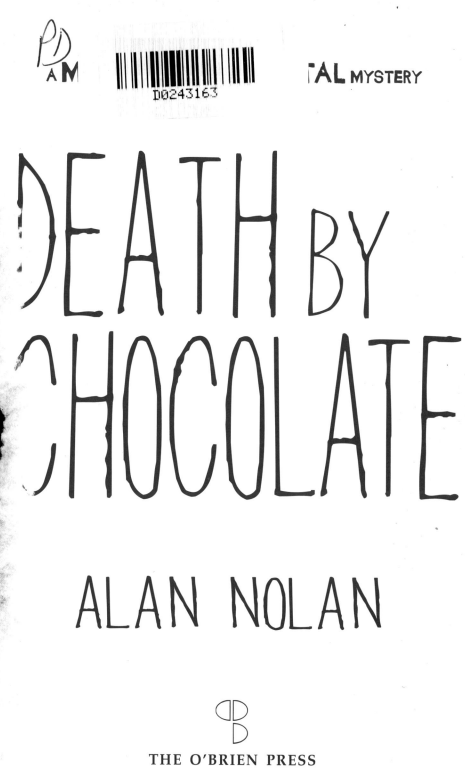

THE O'BRIEN PRESS
DUBLIN

FOR GEORGE AND JEAN
WITH LOVE AND THANKS

First published 2011 by The O'Brien Press Ltd
12 Terenure Road East, Rathgar, Dublin 6, Ireland
Tel: +353 1 4923333; Fax: +353 1 4922777
Email: books @ obrien.ie
Website: www.obrien.ie

ISBN: 978-1-84717-254-9
Copyright for text, illustrations and layout design © Alan Nolan 2011

A catalogue record for this title is available from the British Library

1 2 3 4 5 6
11 12 13 14

The O'Brien Press receives assistance from

Editing: The O'Brien Press Ltd
Printing: Thomson Litho Ltd

DEATH BY CHOCOLATE

Marcel Petit-Pois, you are invited to a Murder.
The Chocolate Bar, Dublin.
October 17th, 8pm Sharp.
I challenge you to stop me... you NITWIT.

Signed: The Chocolatier.

Hey - how ya doin'?

The name is **Tesla**.

Named after Nicolas Tesla, scientific genius, inventor of the X-ray, and all round good egg.

I am P.A., special advisor, and, I'd like to think, friend to **Monsieur Marcel Petit-Pois**, the famous Swiss detective.

You must have heard of him.

He's famous.

Hmm? What's that? The hairy fingers?

I was undur the impression the natural look was **IN** for us gals.

Long story.

Short version.

I'm a chimp.

Not just any chimp, though.

Oh, no.

The second cleverest chimp in Europe.

The first cleverest is my brother,
Caractacus - he can actually speak.

I'm more the sultry, silent type.

But can Caractacus type 120 words a minute while
peeling a grapefruit with his feet?

I think not.

He may have the gift of the yakety-yak, but he
ain't half the chimp his sister is when it comes
to multitasking.

Or **solving crime.**

MARCEL PETIT-POIS
PRIVATE INVESTIGATOR

9

18

21

And so begins another escapade for the famous Swiss detective.

The man who solved the 'Seven Metre Bonsai' mystery.

The man who rescued the shampoo heiress Broadway Monaghan from the clutches of the dastardly Baron Von Geldenheimer.

The man who apprehended the 'Creosote Killer'.

The man who – (and I shouldn't really be telling you this, so keep it to yourselves...) – The man who wears spats on his shoes to cover up the fact that they close with velcro strips because he can't tie his own shoelaces.

True.

It was **me** who solved the 'Bonsai' mystery! It only looked seven metres high because of the hidden magnifying window!

I rescued the heiress! We still swop makeup tips and she sent me a pedicure set for Christmas!

And **I** caught the 'Creosote Killer'! He turned out to be a fence who came to a sticky end!

All me!

Not the great Petit-Pois, as the papers would have you believe.

Not that I'm bitter.

Petit-Pois is a nice guy really.

He just needs a shove in the right direction sometimes.

And sometimes he just needs a shove.

WILLKOMMEN Nach BERLIN!

27

28

Two murders in two days.

My nerves were as shattered as my opera glasses were after Minna Vogelsang's 'singing'.

Did you know the name Vogelsang translates from German as 'birdsong'?

Actually, now that I think of it, that name suits the old turkey!

We'd been to Berlin but were no closer to catching The Chocolatier.

Who was he? Why did he use sweets and chocolate to kill? How did he anticipate our every move? Was he following us? And was that falling sandbag an accident... or **attempted murder?**

I gotta get my thinking cap on, and fast.

My old grandpappy had a saying:

'You have to climb the tallest tree to reach the sweetest coconut.'

Nope. I may be the second smartest chimp in Europe, but I don't know what that means either.

RECEPCIÓN A ESPAÑA!

Malaga

43

48

51

I'm still drying my fur till this day after that dunking.

There are three things that us chimps don't like:

Water, water, and lastly but not leastly, water.

This is why there are very few chimps in the Olympics.

Apart from a few shaved ones in the gymnastics events of course.

WET YOUR WHISTLE IN MOROCCO!

59

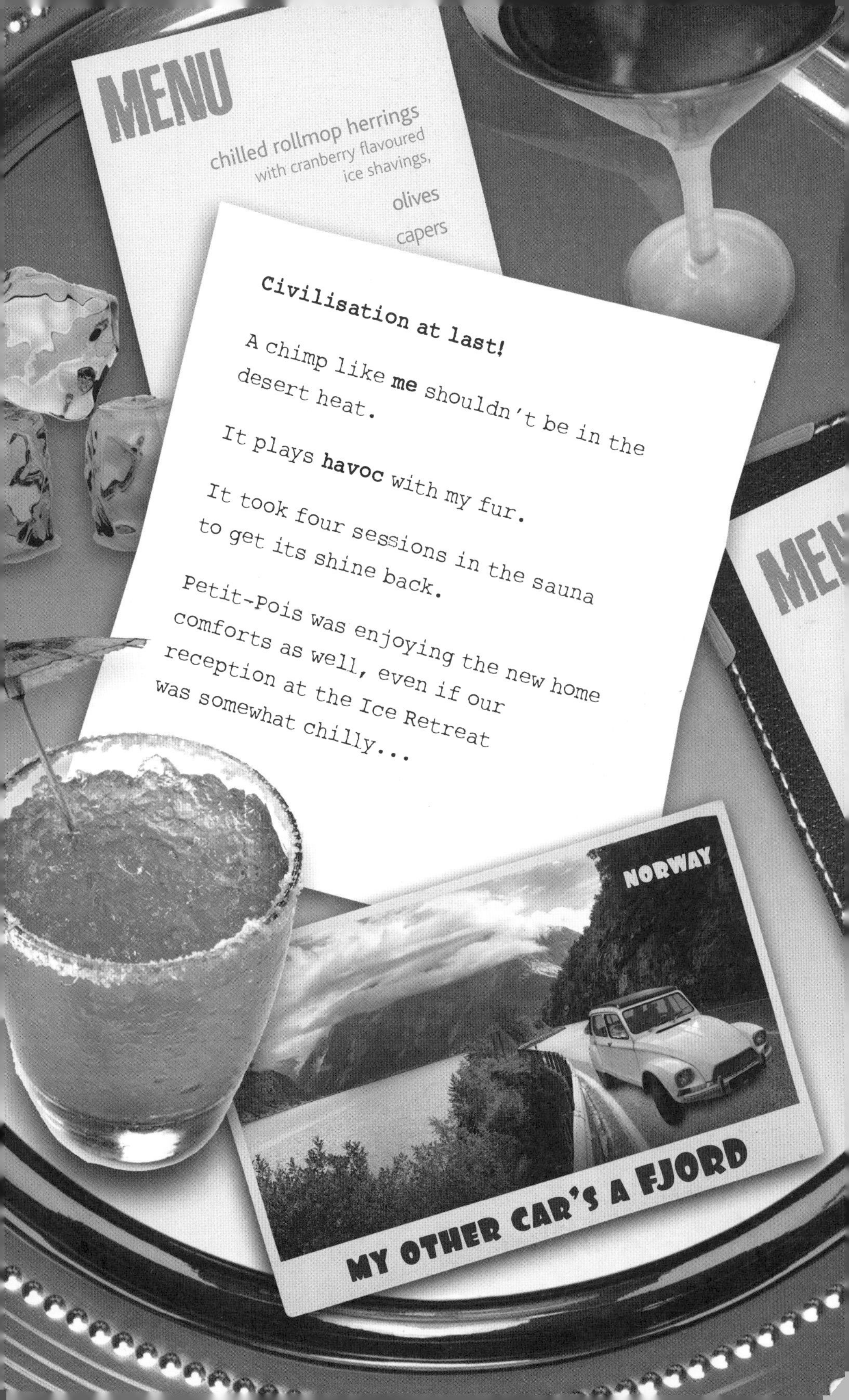

chilled rollmop herrings
with cranberry flavoured
ice shavings,

olives

capers

Civilisation at last!

A chimp like **me** shouldn't be in the desert heat.

It plays **havoc** with my fur.

It took four sessions in the sauna to get its shine back.

Petit-Pois was enjoying the new home comforts as well, even if our reception at the Ice Retreat was somewhat chilly...

MEN

NORWAY

MY OTHER CAR'S A FJORD

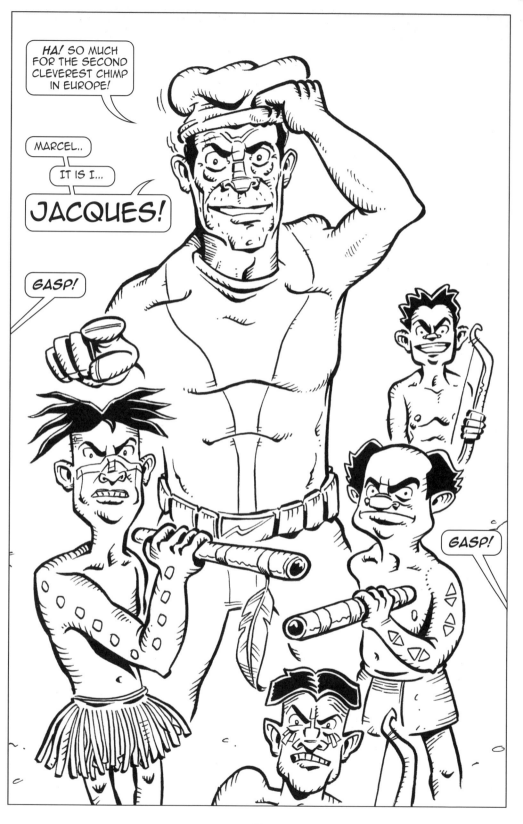

And that's it. **The end.**

We had a lot of explaining to do to the Norwegian authorities.

At least Petit-Pois and Minna did. I played dumb.

Heh.

Petit-Pois was inconsolable for a while. Although Jacques was a nasty piece of work, he was Petit-Pois' brother. And a brother is a brother after all.

Minna went back to the opera. She's currently playing Cio-Cio San in Madame Butterfly in Vienna.

I'd say that's a blast.

Plenty of windows in the Vienna Opera House.

And me?

Let's just say that after all we had been through, Marcel had no option but to change my job title from personal assistant... to **PARTNER.**

Hah!

His **SILENT** partner!

jam
bananas
peanuts
hair oil
moustache wax
12 croissants
  (low calorie)
stamps

MARCEL PETIT-POIS

PRIVATE INVESTIGATOR

TESLA

PRIVATE INVESTIGATOR

*Out to lunch,
back soon!*

ORIGINAL CHARACTER SKETCHES

Alan Nolan lives and works in Bray, County Wicklow, Ireland. He is co-creator (with Ian Whelan) of SANCHO comic, which was shortlisted for two Eagle awards, and is writer and illustrator of the SKREWY SCIENCE WITH PROF. BUTTERKNUT & KRONK cartoon strip for the *Irish Times*. He is the author and illustrator of *The Big Break Detectives Casebook* and the 'Murder Can Be Fatal Mysteries' (The O'Brien Press).

Special thanks to Helen, Michael, Emma, Ivan and all at The O'Brien Press, and to my long-suffering family, Rachel, Adam, Matthew and Sam.

www.murdercanbefatal.com

www.alannolan.ie